Quick-Fix Blen

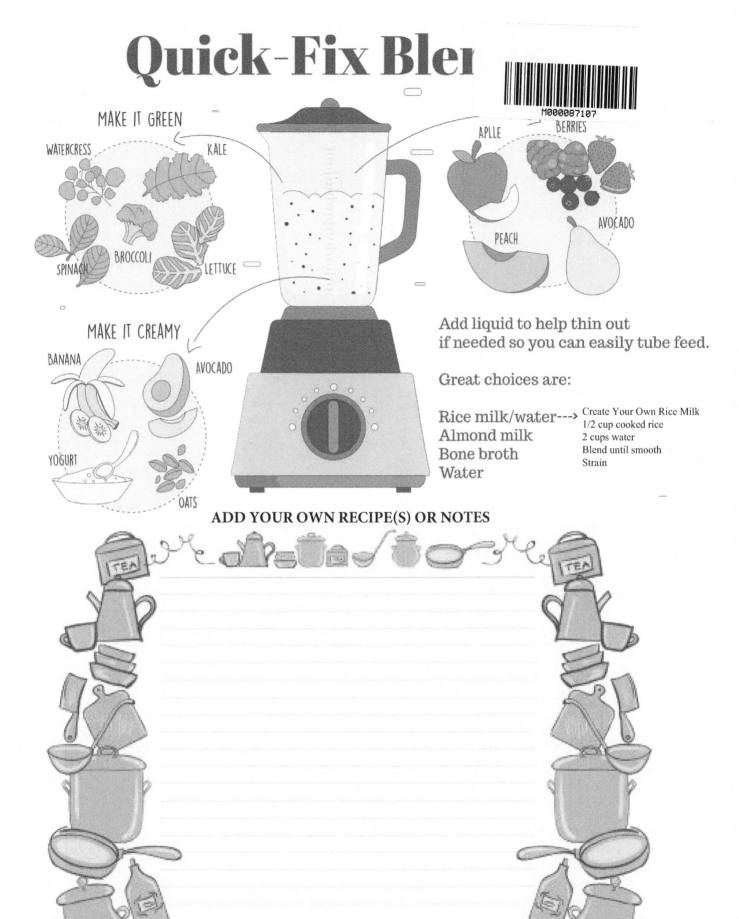

MAKE IT GREEN

WATERCRESS KALE SPINACH BROCCOLI LETTUCE

APLLE BERRIES PEACH AVOCADO

MAKE IT CREAMY

BANANA AVOCADO YOGURT OATS

Add liquid to help thin out
if needed so you can easily tube feed.

Great choices are:

Rice milk/water--->
Almond milk
Bone broth
Water

Create Your Own Rice Milk
1/2 cup cooked rice
2 cups water
Blend until smooth
Strain

ADD YOUR OWN RECIPE(S) OR NOTES

Any Known Food Allergies List Here

Notes

MEALS / FOOD

MISCELLANEOUS

ME TIME - READ, WALK, RELAX, SPA, ETC	IMPORTANT STUFF	NOTES/REMINDERS	APPOINTMENTS	GROCERY SHOPPING	PREPARE BLENDED MEALS
					M
					T
					W
					T
					F
					S
					S

MONDAY

TUESDAY

WEDNESDAY

THURSDAY

FRIDAY

SATURDAY-SUNDAY

♥ MONDAY

JUST STUFF

♥ TUESDAY

♥ WEDNESDAY

GOALS

♥ THURSDAY

♥ FRIDAY

♥ SATURDAY / SUNDAY

DETOX WATER

— INGREDIENTS —

10-12 MINT LEAVES   2 LEMONS

3 QTS. WATER   1/2 CUCUMBER

Put these ingredients in a mason jar and let it sit out at room temperature for at least 24 hours and then strain before feeding. One favorite is to blend all the ingredients in a blender and strain.

No matter how you prepare your detox water make sure you strain it before tube feeding. If you strain good enough, you should be able to administer this water via a feeding pump machine without any problems.

Create Your Own Water Detox

Recipe

Directions

_____

_____

_____

_____

_____

_____

Ingredients

_____

_____

_____

_____

_____

_____

_____

_____

MONDAY

TUESDAY

WEDNESDAY

THURSDAY

FRIDAY

SATURDAY / SUNDAY

JUST STUFF

GOALS

List Favorite Foods

Notes

Recipe

Date _____

Prep _____

Total _____

Syringe or Machine - Both _____

Ingredients

Directions

arugula parsley rosemary bay canella

dill oregano basil chili

ginger black pepper star anise vanilla clove spice

LISTED ARE SOME POWERFUL HERBS YOU SHOULD CONSIDER USING. CREATE A FEW
RECIPES AROUND SOME OF THE HERBS LISTED ABOVE.

Recipe

Directions

Ingredients

.RECIPE.

Ingredients

Instructions

Recipe

Recipe

Instructions

Ingredients

Recipe

Ingredients

Recipe

Ingredients

What is your plan for this week?

Wednesday

Tuesday

Monday

Sunday

Additional Notes

Saturday

Friday

Thursday

What is your plan for this week?

Wednesday

Tuesday

Monday

Sunday

Aditional Notes

Saturday

Friday

Thursday

What is your plan for this week?

Wednesday

Tuesday

Monday

Sunday

Additional Notes

Saturday

Friday

Thursday

What is your plan for this week?

Sunday

Monday

Tuesday

Wednesday

Thursday

Friday

Saturday

Additional Notes

What is your plan for this week?

Sunday

Monday

Tuesday

Wednesday

Thursday

Friday

Saturday

Aditional Notes

Notes

Recipe

Date _____

Prep _____

Total _____

Syringe
or Machine - Both _____

Ingredients

Directions

MAKE IT HOW YOU LIKE
AND CREATE YOUR OWN

ORANGE

RASPBERRY

HONEY

YOGURT

**BLEND
ADD WATER
STRAIN**

Recipe
Directions
_____
_____
_____
_____
_____
_____
_____
_____

Ingredients
_____
_____
_____
_____
_____
_____
_____
_____

·RECIPE·

Ingredients	Instructions
_____	_____
_____	_____
_____	_____
_____	_____
_____	_____
_____	_____

Recipe _____
_____
_____
_____
_____
_____
_____
_____

Recipe

Instructions
_____
_____
_____
_____
_____

Ingredients
_____
_____
_____
_____
_____

Recipe
_____
_____
_____
_____
_____

Ingredients
_____
_____
_____
_____

Recipe _____
_____
_____
_____
_____
_____
_____
_____
_____

Ingredients

Notes

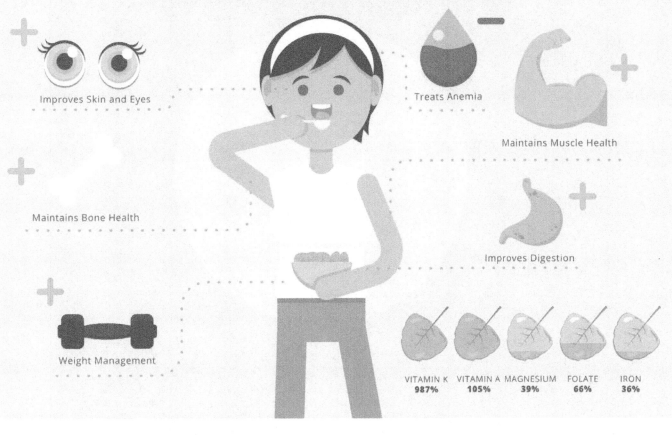

SPINANCH BENEFITS

Improves Skin and Eyes

Maintains Bone Health

Weight Management

Treats Anemia

Maintains Muscle Health

Improves Digestion

VITAMIN K	VITAMIN A	MAGNESIUM	FOLATE	IRON
987%	105%	39%	66%	36%

CREATE BLENDED RECIPES WITH SPINANCH

Recipe
Directions

Ingredients

RECIPE

Ingredients

Instructions

Recipe

Recipe

Instructions

Ingredients

Recipe

Ingredients

Recipe

Ingredients

Notes

HEALTH BENEFITS
ORANGE

Heart Health
Immune Support
Digestive Health
Alkalizing
Cholesterol Lowering
Healthy Skin
Kidney Support
Anti Inflammatory
Anti Cancer
Vision Protection

HEALTH BENEFITS
MANGOS

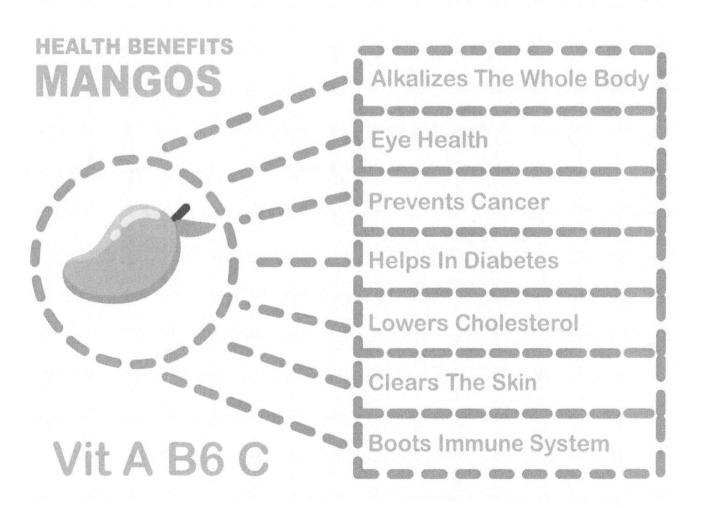

Vit A B6 C

Alkalizes The Whole Body

Eye Health

Prevents Cancer

Helps In Diabetes

Lowers Cholesterol

Clears The Skin

Boots Immune System

BENEFIT OF CRANBERRIES

Excellent Source of
VITAMIN C + E

Good Source of
VITAMIN A + K

CHOLESTEROL FREE

Saturated FAT FREE

Very Low in SODIUM

HEALTH BENEFITS
GRAPE

Fight Diabetes

Diarrhetic

Prevents Cancer

Anti Aging

Anti Inflammatory

High Anti Oxidants

Lowers Blood Pressure

Support Muscle Repair

Prevents Hearts Attacks

Increases Good Cholesterol

Salads Cheat Sheet

To make these salads so it can be given via a feeding tube, you will need to add water, broth, etc to thin it out. Don't forget to strain.

 **tomato**

 **tomato**

tomato

cucumber

 cucumber

feta cheese

cheese

olive ⁰⁰

onion

pepper

olive ⁰⁰

 cucumber

almonds

parmesan cheese

chicken

avocado

bread

bacon

bread

egg

carrot

onion

olive ⁰⁰

bread

 lettuce

 lettuce

lettuce

lettuce

lettuce

 lettuce

 lettuce

GREEK SALAD   CAESAR SALAD   COBB SALAD   GARDEN SALAD

Notes

List all medications and refill dates

Rx

Pharmacy Name _____

Address/Phone_____

_____

_____

PRESCRIPTIONS:

_____

_____

_____

_____

_____

_____

_____

_____

_____

List all medications and refill dates

R

Pharmacy Name _____

Address/Phone_____

_____

PRESCRIPTIONS:

_____

_____

_____

_____

_____

_____

_____

_____

_____

Super Foods To Add To Your Blended Diet

Fruits

1. Cantaloupe

Only a quarter of cantaloupe provides almost all the vitamin A needed in one day. Since the beta-carotene in a cantaloupe converts to vitamin A, you get both nutrients at once. These vision-strengthening nutrients may help reduce the risk of developing cataracts. Like an orange, cantaloupe is also an excellent source of vitamin C, which helps our immune system. It is also is a good source of vitamin B6, dietary fiber, folate, niacin, and potassium, which helps maintain good blood sugar levels and metabolism. This pale orange power fruit may help reduce our risk of heart disease, stroke, and cancer.

2. Blueberries

These mildly sweet (and sometimes tangy) berries offer a high capacity to destroy free radicals that can cause cancer. Low in calories, they offer antioxidant phytonutrients called anthocyanidins, which enhance the effects of vitamin C. These antioxidants may help prevent cataracts, glaucoma, varicose veins, hemorrhoids, peptic ulcers, heart disease and cancer.

Vegetables

3: Tomatoes

Tomatoes help us fight against heart disease and cancers such as colorectal, prostate, breast, endometrial, lung, and cancer of the pancreas. Tomatoes are also good sources of vitamin C, A, and K. In a 2004 study, it was found that tomato juice alone can help reduce blood clotting.

Fresh, organic tomatoes deliver three times as much of the cancer-fighting carotenoid lycopene. Even organic ketchup is better for you than regular ketchup! Look for tomato pastes and sauces that contain the whole tomato (including peels) because you will absorb 75% more lycopene and almost two times the amount of beta-carotene.

4: Sweet Potatoes

As an excellent source of vitamin A, C, and manganese, sweet potatoes are also a good source of copper, dietary fiber, vitamin B6, potassium and iron. Those who are smokers or prone to second- hand smoke may benefit greatly from this root vegetable that helps protect us against emphysema.

For a unique dessert, cube a cooked sweet potato and slice a banana. Then lightly pour maple syrup over the top and add a dash or two of cinnamon. Add chopped walnuts for an even healthier kick. Blend together with some rice milk until smooth, strain if needed and bolus feed. Yummy!

5: Spinach and Kale

A cancer-fighter and cardio-helper, spinach and kale top the list as far as green leafy vegetables are concerned. Much like broccoli, they provide an excellent source of vitamin A and C. Kale is a surprisingly good source of calcium at 25% per cup, boiled. Vitamin K is abundantly found in spinach as well, with almost 200% of the Daily Value available, to help reduce bone loss.

Whole Grains

6: Whole Grain Bread, Pasta and Brown Rice

Whether it's bread or pasta, the first thing to check for when purchasing whole grain bread and pasta is to make sure it is 100% whole grain. Remember to check the list of ingredients on the package. For example, look for the exact phrase "whole wheat flour" as one of the first ingredients listed in whole wheat bread. If it's not listed as such, then it's not whole grain. Wheat bran is a cancer-fighting grain that also helps us regulate our bowel movements.

Brown rice is also a better choice than refined grain (white rice) for the same reason as choosing whole wheat bread. Whole wheat flour or brown rice that turns into white flour or white rice actually destroys between 50-90% of vitamin B3, vitamin B1, vitamin B6, manganese, phosphorus, iron, and all of the dietary fiber and essential fatty acids we need. Even when processed white flour or white rice is "enriched," it is not in the same form as the original unprocessed kind. In fact, 11 nutrients are actually lost and are not replaced during the "enrichment" process!

Nuts

7: Walnuts

These nuts are packed with omega-3 fats, which is one of the "good" fats. A quarter cup of walnuts would take care of about 90% of the omega-3s needed in one day. Walnuts provide many health benefits including cardiovascular protection, better cognitive function, anti-inflammatory advantages relating to asthma, rheumatoid arthritis, and inflammatory skin diseases like eczema and psoriasis. They can even help against cancer and also support the immune system.

Beans and Legumes

8: Black Beans and Lentils

While black beans are a good source of fiber that can lower cholesterol, so are lentils. The high fiber content in both black beans and lentils helps to maintain blood sugar levels. Also a fat-free, high quality protein with additional minerals and B-vitamins, black beans and lentils fill you up and don't expand your waistline.

A complete, one-stop source of using a variety of beans and lentils comes easy when you can find a bag of 15-bean mix (includes black beans, lentils, navy, pinto, red, kidney, etc.) at the grocery store. Consider making a delicious tube feeding blended soup with the addition of tomatoes, onions, garlic and your favorite spices with this bean mixture.

Dairy

9: Skim Milk and Yogurt

Skim milk (or low-fat) helps to promote strong bones, offering an excellent source of calcium, vitamin D, and vitamin K. These nutrients help protect colon cells from cancer-causing chemicals, bone loss, migraine headaches, premenstrual symptoms, and childhood obesity. Recent studies also show that overweight adults lose weight, especially around the midsection, when consuming low-fat dairy such as skim milk and yogurt.

Yogurt also includes the essential nutrients such as phosphorous and vitamin B2, vitamin B12, vitamin B5, zinc, potassium, and protein. Yogurt's live bacterial cultures also provide a wealth of health benefits that may help us live longer and strengthen our immune system.

Seafood

10: Salmon

Salmon is high in protein, low in saturated fat and high in omega-3 fats (the essential fatty acids that are also found in those walnuts mentioned earlier). Salmon is a heart-healthy food and is recommended to eat at least twice a week. When choosing salmon, it's best to stay away from farm raised and select wild instead. Research studies show that farmed salmon may cause cancer because it may carry high levels of carcinogenic chemicals known as polychlorinated biphenyls (PCBs).

Other

Green Tea and "Power" Water

Although not food per say, the health benefits of these beverages are worthy of mentioning.

Green tea has beneficial phytonutrients and lower levels of caffeine than all other teas. The more research studying green tea, the more health benefits are found. A cancer fighter as well, green tea has antioxidant effects that lower risks of bacterial or viral infections to cardiovascular disease, cancer, stroke, periodontal disease, and osteoporosis.

Water packed with vitamins and/or naturally sweetened fruit are also the newest trend. Some offer a full day's supply of vitamin C while others promise no artificial sweeteners with a full, fruity taste.

As you can see, the top ten super foods are worth every bite (or sip). Now that you know which foods can help save your life, what's more important than investing in your health?

GREEN BLENDED RECIPES

One of the central components of any healthy blended diet is consuming a sufficient quantity of greens. Yet 95% of people who follow a blended diet, do not consume enough green leafy vegetables.

Why green foods are so important?

A substance that is found in all plants is Chlorophyll. What it does is it acts as a blood detoxifier, which helps increase circulation to all your organs. It does this by dilating blood vessels and it is also a natural deodorant because it helps reduce offensive body oder.

Super greens can help boost your immune system they are powerful antioxidants, that can help you grow and have many another health benefits as well. Bottom line is super greens are one of the greatest things you can do to your body.

Here are a few good green blended recipe ideas.

Berry Roman

1 cup strawberries

2 whole bananas

1/2 bunch romaine

1 to 2 cups water

Blend fruit, water, add romaine lettuce. Strain if needed. Bolus feed with syringe.

Spinach Delight

2 cups fresh spinach

1 whole grated cucumber or carrot

2 whole bananas

1 whole orange

3 whole peeled apples

Blend together all ingredients until smooth. Strain if needed. Bolus feed with syringe.

Blended Salads

By now you've gotten used to adding greens to your blended meals, you can graduate to making blended salads! Yum. You can transition gradually by reducing the amount of fruit in your blends and increasing the quantity of greens.

2 medium tomatoes, roughly chopped

2 ribs of celery

2-4 cups very finely chopped kale

1 big handful spinach

1 green onion

1/2 avocado

1/4 cup parsley

1 cup of water or more if needed

Blend the tomatoes together, and add the rest of the ingredients. Use water to help thin the blend out. You might need less or more water. Therefore I recommend that you always blend your ingredients first as much as you can, then gradually add water until you get the right blended consistency you desire. Bolus feed with syringe.

Notes

♥ MONDAY

♥ TUESDAY

♥ WEDNESDAY

♥ THURSDAY

♥ FRIDAY

♥ SATURDAY / SUNDAY

JUST STUFF

GOALS

Notes

Notes

Notes

Notes

Notes

Notes

Notes

Notes

Notes

Notes

Notes

Notes

Notes

Notes

Notes

Notes

MEALS / FOOD

MISCELLANEOUS

ME TIME - READ, WALK, RELAX, SPA, ETC	IMPORTANT STUFF	NOTES/REMINDERS	APPOINTMENTS	GROCERY SHOPPING	PREPARE BLENDED MEALS
					M
					T
					W
					T
					F
					S
					S

MONDAY

TUESDAY

WEDNESDAY

THURSDAY

FRIDAY

SATURDAY-SUNDAY

MEALS / FOOD

MISCELLANEOUS

ME TIME - READ, WALK, RELAX, SPA, ETC	IMPORTANT STUFF	NOTES/REMINDERS	APPOINTMENTS	GROCERY SHOPPING	PREPARE BLENDED MEALS
					M
					T
					W
					T
					F
					S
					S

MONDAY

TUESDAY

WEDNESDAY

THURSDAY

FRIDAY

SATURDAY-SUNDAY

MEALS / FOOD

MISCELLANEOUS

ME TIME - READ, WALK, RELAX, SPA, ETC	IMPORTANT STUFF	NOTES/REMINDERS	APPOINTMENTS	GROCERY SHOPPING	PREPARE BLENDED MEALS
					M
					T
					W
					T
					F
					S
					S

MONDAY

TUESDAY

WEDNESDAY

THURSDAY

FRIDAY

SATURDAY-SUNDAY

MEALS / FOOD

MISCELLANEOUS

ME TIME - READ, WALK, RELAX, SPA, ETC	IMPORTANT STUFF	NOTES/REMINDERS	APPOINTMENTS	GROCERY SHOPPING	PREPARE BLENDED MEALS
					M
					T
					W
					T
					F
					S
					S

MONDAY

TUESDAY

WEDNESDAY

THURSDAY

FRIDAY

SATURDAY-SUNDAY

MEALS / FOOD

MISCELLANEOUS

ME TIME - READ, WALK, RELAX, SPA, ETC	IMPORTANT STUFF	NOTES/REMINDERS	APPOINTMENTS	GROCERY SHOPPING	PREPARE BLENDED MEALS
					M
					T
					W
					T
					F
					S
					S

MONDAY

TUESDAY

WEDNESDAY

THURSDAY

FRIDAY

SATURDAY-SUNDAY

MONTH_____ YEAR_____

SUNDAY	MONDAY	TUESDAY	WEDNESDAY	THRUSDAY	FRIDAY	SATURDAY

MONTH_____ YEAR_____

SUNDAY	MONDAY	TUESDAY	WEDNESDAY	THRUSDAY	FRIDAY	SATURDAY

MONTH_____ YEAR_____

SUNDAY	MONDAY	TUESDAY	WEDNESDAY	THRUSDAY	FRIDAY	SATURDAY

MONTH_____ YEAR_____

SUNDAY	MONDAY	TUESDAY	WEDNESDAY	THRUSDAY	FRIDAY	SATURDAY

Recipe

Date _____

Prep _____

Total _____

Syringe
or Machine - Both _____

Ingredients

Directions

Recipe

_____

Date _____

Prep _____

Total _____

**Syringe
or Machine - Both** _____

Directions

Ingredients

Recipe

Date _____

Prep _____

Total _____

Syringe or Machine - Both _____

Ingredients

Directions

Recipe

_____

Date _____

Prep _____

Total _____

Syringe _____
or Machine - Both

Directions

Ingredients

Recipe

Date _____

Prep _____

Total _____

Syringe _____
or Machine - Both

Ingredients

Directions

Recipe

_____

Date _____

Prep _____

Total _____

Syringe or Machine - Both

Ingredients

Directions

Recipe

_____

Date _____

Prep _____

Total _____

Syringe or Machine - Both _____

Ingredients

Directions

Recipe

Date _____

Prep _____

Total _____

Syringe
or Machine - Both _____

Ingredients

Directions

Recipe

Date _____

Prep _____

Total _____

Syringe or Machine - Both _____

Ingredients

Directions

Recipe

_____

Date _____

Prep _____

Total _____

Syringe _____
or Machine - Both

Directions

Ingredients

Made in the USA
Middletown, DE
19 September 2022

10784236R00064